KAMA PUA'A

Adventures of
KAMA PUA'A

By Guy & Pam Buffet
Illustrated by Guy Buffet
Edited by Ruth Tabrah

An Island Heritage Book

Produced and published by Island Heritage Limited
Norfolk Island, Australia

Copyright © 1972 Island Heritage Limited
ALL RIGHTS RESERVED
Library of Congress Catalog Number 72-76459
ISBN Trade 0-8348-3002-7
This edition first published in Japan

For the Island Heritage distributor in your area,
please write or phone:

Island Heritage Limited (USA)
Editorial Offices
1020 Auahi St. Bldg. 3
Honolulu, Hawaii 96814
Phone: (808) 531-5091
Cable: HAWAIIBOOK

Engraving, printing, and binding by
Dai Nippon Printing Co., (Hong Kong) Ltd. Hong Kong

An Island Heritage Book

anne Name? annie

For Connie and Bob

Kama-puaʻa was a Hawaiian god. He was born on the island of Kauai where his parents, Hina and Kahiki-ʻula, had been told to expect a very special child.

Even with this warning, Kahiki-ʻula fainted away when he first saw his newborn son.

"A pig, no matter how special, is no child of mine!"
he said when he revived. "Take him from my
sight forever!"

Covered with a ti-leaf cape, Kama-puaʻa was taken across the channel to the island of Oahu to live with his mother's mother, Ka-maunu-a-niho.

She greeted the little pig with a loving smile. "Come with me, my grandson. I will take you home and tell you who you are."

His grandmother led Kama-pua'a to a clifftop. She opened her hands to the sky and chanted. . .

"You are a special child. You are Kama-pua'a! Sometimes a man, sometimes a boar. You have magic powers. You are a kupua. You can be many things!"

"A handsome boy, strong and skillful in hunting, fishing, fighting. So clever you might be tempted to play tricks on people."

"The biggest and strongest boar in the universe,
Or a small pig,
Or many pigs at once!"

"You can be the leaf of the hiwa, the white shoot of the kikea plant, or a kukui tree."

"Should you have to escape through the sea, you can even be a humu-humu-nuku-nuku-a-pua-'a!"

"You can live here in Ka-liu-wa'a valley as long as you like," said his grandmother, her chant ended. "Come and go as you please. Should you need to use these magic powers, call me and I will help you. One warning! Never indulge your appetite! Remember, a pig can eat his way to helplessness.

"Ah," she said, pleased. "You feel like being a boy now. And you are, just as you can be any of those things I have chanted to you."

Next morning, Kama-pua'a climbed a hill that overlooked Chief Olopana's village in Punalu'u. "So many chickens down there," said the pig-boy with a sly, hungry grin.

That night when he crept down to steal some of the village chickens, Kama-pua`a saw a big, fierce rooster — Chief Olopana's prize possession.

Kama-puaʻa didn't know this bird was the favorite of the powerful chief.

The second night, when he crept down again to the sleeping village, Kama-pua'a took the rooster by surprise and ran off with him.

Next morning when Chief Olopana found his prize bird missing, he sent men to search out and catch the thief.

As they hunted, the men caught a glimpse of
Kama-pua‘a in the forest. He had taken the rooster to
his grandmother's house.

Kama-pua`a darted behind a bush.
The men followed. No boy to be seen —
only a big black pig.

When Chief Olopana was told this strange tale, he sent for Lono-a-ohi, his kahuna. "That boy must be Kama-pua'a," said the priest. "He is a clever kupua. He can change from pig to man to many things!"

The next night, more chickens were stolen from the village. Olopana's men followed the trail of feathers and found Kama-pua'a sleeping. They quickly bound his feet and tied him to a pole.

As they carried him off, Kama-pua'a cried out, "Grandmother! Make me the biggest boar in the universe!"

Chief Olopana was furious. With all his army, he went to invade Ka-liu-waʻa valley, to capture Kama-puaʻa, and to get his prize rooster back.

He and his men pursued the pig-boy and his grand-mother through the dense forest. Branches reached out to trip Olopana and his warriors. High boughs rubbed together making eerie sounds. Mysterious power seemed to lurk in every shadow. Olopana's men were frightened, but the Chief drove them on.

At the head of the valley was a steep cliff. "Aole pilikia," said Ka-maunu-a-niho. She chanted until Kama-pua'a became so huge she could use his bristles as a ladder to escape.

Kama-pua'a dragged himself up over the cliff. His back gouged a deep rut in the stone. Out gushed Sacred Falls, which can still be seen on windward Oahu.

The giant pig and his grandmother fled to Wahiawa, where they had relatives, and where the rooster was hidden away.

At first, Kama-pua'a's size frightened everyone. His grandmother explained that the boar was a cousin from Kauai. Soon the children were all playing with Kama-pua'a, climbing on him and tickling his snout.

In Punaluʻu, the defeated chief grew angrier. He called for a new kahuna, a Kauai priest said to know the secret weakness of Kama-puaʻa.

Chief Olopana had his old kahuna, Lono-a-ohi, tied to a stake. "When I capture him I will sacrifice you and the pig-boy together!"

Malae, the new kahuna, first had Olopana move his entire village to Wahiawa.

In a clearing near Kama-pua'a's relatives, Malae had
the chief's men gather an enormous pile of food — fish,
chickens, 'awa, bananas, taro — everything to tempt a
giant pig's appetite.

The scent of the food soon led Kama-puaʻa to the clearing. He ate and ate until there was no more. He was so full he could not move. He was so full he could not make a sound.

Olopana's men leapt from their hiding places and bound him. Ka-maunu-a-niho tried to help by making her powerless grandson smaller, but Malae was ready for her tricks. He had the men keep tightening the ropes.

Kama-pua`a was placed on the sacrificial altar with the old kahuna. They were to die at dawn. All night, the constellation of the Boar gazed down at them. "That is a good sign," said Lono-a-ohi hopefully.

At dawn, Chief Olopana and his men entered the temple. They knelt before the altar where the two

captives lay. Kama-pua'a had regained his strength
but pretended he was still helpless.

Suddenly, with a tremendous roar, he became an eight-eyed, eight-legged monster with long shining teeth!

Olopana and his men tried to flee. They could not. Overwhelmed with fear, they were turned to stone.

Freed, Lono-a-ohi walked gratefully from the temple.
Kama-pua'a walked beside him, once again a handsome
boy with mischief in his eyes.

A pig? A giant boar? Many pigs? The leaf of the hiwa
or the white shoot of the kikea plant or a kukui tree?
A humu-humu-nuku-nuku-apua'a? Who knew what
he would be next? Who knew what he would do?

An Introduction to Things Hawaiian

Most of the Hawaiian names and words used in this book have a special, symbolic meaning in the Kamapua'a (Kah-mah-poo-ah-ah) legends. There are six major legends. This is the first.

Kamapua'a is the Hawaiian expression of the sacredness of the boar. The boar in ancient India was the vehicle of the god Vishnu and a form of the god Rudra. He appears in India and throughout Oceania with plants on his back — medicinal plants which were forms the boar could magically assume, as well as substitutes which could replace him in a sacrifice.

Kamapua'a's plant forms were kikea (kee-kay-ah), the white ti stalk, *cord-*

White Ti

yline terminalis, and kukui (koo-koo-wee)the candlenut tree, *molucca aleurites*.

Kukui

Kamapua'a was a kupua (koo-poo-ah), a shape-shifter. Unlike the wizards of European lore, the kupua could only shift to a certain defined range of forms dependent on his ancestral origin, his clan relationships, his specific interdependence with other symbols or beings.

The name of Kamapua'a's grandmother signifies she is a sorceress. Hawai-

Kupua

ian is a language rich in puns and double meanings. Ka-maunu-a-niho (Kah-mow-noo-ah-nee-ho) is from maunu-bait and niho-teeth, bones, or personal belongings — the everlasting parts of the body that are used as "bait" by a sorcerer. It is a name bestowing supernatural power. The family name Kamaunu or Kamaunu-nui means "forever continuing" or "great progeny". Niho here could also refer to the boar's tusk.

Hina

The names of Kamapua'a's parents are likewise symbolic. Hina (Hee-nah) has a double meaning as the grayish shine of gray hair or the moon. It is also the name of the Hawaiian goddess of the moon, patron deity of fishermen and so perhaps distantly related to the fish form possible to Kamapua'a, humu-humu-nuku-niku-a-pua-a (hoo-moo-hoo-moo-noo-koo-noo-koo-ah-poo-ah-ah) a trigger fish of patchwork color pattern (humuhumu-to sew pieces together) with the snout (nukunuku) of a pig (pua'a).

Ka-hiki-'ula (kah-hee-kee-oo-lah), the name of Kamapua'a's father, means "red-

Tahiti". Red is the sacred color denoting the chiefs of the red feather girdle of Tahiti.

Kahuna

The kahuna (kah-hoo-nah) was the priest who advised the chief and conducted all temple worship. His knowledge was hidden, esoteric. The name of Olopana's kahuna Lono-a-ohi (Low-no-ah-oh-hee) could refer to Kamapua'a being

Hiwa

all of the various manifestations of Lono, god of agriculture. Ohi (oh-hee) is the special word for a young pig. Malae (Mah-lye), the name of the kahuna who knew Kamapua'a's secret weakness, may refer to the Polynesian word malae, a clearing, a place set aside for sacred worship. Tahitian marae.

Hiwa (hee-vah) was a blackness associated with high social rank, a sacred color esteemed in sacrifice. A black pig was considered the most acceptable sacrifice to the gods.

Olopana

Olopana (oh-low-pah-nah) was the king of the island of Oahu (oh-ah-hoo), the central island of the Hawaiian archipelago where most of this story takes place. Olopana was also chief of the district of Punaluu (Poo-nah-loo-oo) which means spring-to-dive, a pond into which one can plunge, and which is still the name of that windward Oahu district. Kauai, or Kaua'i (Cow-wah-ee), the island northwest of Oahu where Kamapua'a

was born, has a name so ancient its origin and meaning have been lost.

Ka-liu-waa (kah-lee-oo-vah-ah) means literally the bilge of the canoe, the rutting out of the stone facing of the cliff and collecting water in the basin of Sacred Falls, still known as sacred to Kamapua'a in the windward valley of Ka-liu-waa.

The other four Hawaiian words in this book are common ones. "Awa (ah-vah) is piper methysticum, a shrub whose root is chewed or pounded to make a narcotic drink. Taro (tah-ro) is the starchy plant, colocasia esculenta, the Hawaiian

Taro

food staple cooked and mashed into poi (poy). "Auwe" (ow-way) is the equivalent of "alas!", "what a pity!"; an exclamation of consternation, sorrow, regret, wonder, fear.

"Aole pilikia" (ah-oh-lee pee-lee-kee-ah) means "no trouble" which is what we hope you'll have understanding and pronouncing the Hawaiian in this book.

———————————————

Island Heritage is deeply grateful to
Rubellite K. Johnson for the many
hours she spent so willingly in
helping us present this first volume
of Kamapua'a.

We are also appreciative of the help and
support of Yoshio Hayashi, Chelo Garza,
June Gutmanis, Henk Kuiper and Gwen
Matsui of Master Color Laboratories,
Addressograph-Multigraph Corporation,
and Gene Lewis from Pacific Photo Type.

About the Artists

Pam and Guy Buffet both travelled extensively
before they were twenty, Guy in the French Navy,
and Pam with her family in the import-export
business.

Guy was born in Paris and studied art from the
age of 15 at the Beaux Arts of Toulon. From there
he studied advanced painting at the Acadamie
de Peinture de la Ville de Paris.

In the French Navy he made two round-the-world
trips on the cruisers "De Grasse" and "Jeanne
d'Arc" giving exhibits of his paintings in the name
of French culture in each port. Shortly after this,
Guy spent some time in the Hawaiian Islands,
thus beginning his career in the United States.
In 1964, living in San Francisco, he had one man
shows in Los Angeles, Dallas, and Mexico. In 1968,
in San Francisco, he met and married Pam, an art
major graduate from the University of California.

Buffet's work now hangs in many fine private
collections in Hawaii and on the mainland. He has
done commissions for Fireman's Fund Insurance
Company and the Bank of America. He has just
completed his first mural, a commission from the
Hawaii State Foundation on Culture and the Arts.